StoneSoup

Writing and art by kids, for kids

Editor's Note

Memoir has the spotlight in this issue. In these pages, you will find Georgia Marshall's interview with her grandfather, which is at once a tribute, a biography in miniature, and a thoughtful reflection on what makes a good life. You will find two personal stories, Louise Johnson's "Unconditional" and Misha Joksic's "The Deadly Pain"—both difficult stories to live through and to tell, both fully and beautifully realized. Finally, you will find Noah Xia's "The Magic Desk," a lovely meditation on the object at the center of the writer's creative life. I hope you will read these pieces and be reminded of all the forms and subjects you can address in nonfiction!

Lastly, I want to call attention to this month's incredible cover art by Ivory Vanover, which—in addition to being just a beautiful, intricate painting—captures the way one's mind fills with images and action when reading a very good book, or writing one.

There is so much more amazing work within our pages this month—enjoy it all.

Happy holidays!

On the cover:
Imagination (Watercolor)
Ivory Vanover, 12
Texas

Editor in Chief
Emma Wood

Director
William Rubel

Operations
Sophia Opitz

Design
Joe Ewart

Production Coordinator
Carmela Furio

Blog Editor
Caleb Berg

Customer Service
Tayleigh Greene

Refugee Project
Laura Moran

Stone Soup (ISSN 0094 579X) is published eleven times per year—monthly, with a combined July/August summer issue. Copyright © 2022 by the Children's Art Foundation–Stone Soup Inc., a 501(c)(3) nonprofit organization located in Santa Cruz, California. All rights reserved.

To request the braille edition of *Stone Soup* from the National Library of Congress, call +1 800-424-8567. To request access to the audio edition via the National Federation of the Blind's NFB-NEWSLINE®, call +1 866-504-7300, or visit Nfbnewsline.org.

StoneSoup
Contents

Mountain and Water (Markers)
Jiacheng Yu, 6
Florida

The Story of the Puddle and the Frog

A puddle who yearns to see the ocean beseeches a frog to tell him all about it

By Ava Shorten, 12
Ireland

There was once a river. For years, this river had flowed gently all the way from the top of a great mountain down into a forest, where it joined up with tributaries and eventually ran into the sea.

Until, that is, it stopped. The river had been blocked up with sticks and stones at the place where it ran out of the forest and into the sea. No matter how much the poor river tried, it could not trickle in or around this blockage.

The river began to dry up. The sun became high in the sky, until at last the river was nothing but a puddle in the shade of a large willow tree. The puddle was within sight of the ocean, and every day he yearned to reach it, and yet he couldn't.

One warm summer's evening, a young frog hopped up to the puddle and began to splash around. The puddle spoke to him.

"Have you ever been to the sea?" he asked the frog. The frog looked around in surprise, and then realized it was the puddle speaking.

"Yes," replied the frog. "Many times. Have you?"

"Once I was there every day," said the puddle mournfully. "Until my river was blocked, and I dried up to the size of a puddle. Tell me of it," he begged. "I long every day to be able to flow into its wonderful coolness, and yet I can't."

"Alright," said the frog. "It is a vast, deep-blue blanket that covers the world. In the summertime, the waves are calm and gentle, and dolphins frolic in the shallows. In the spring, willow trees drape their leaves over the rock pools, and fish dance in the waves. In the autumn, colored leaves are blown from afar and come to rest on the choppy waves."

"And what of the winter?" asked the puddle eagerly.

"Ah yes, the winter. In the winter, waves rise as high as mountains and crash down upon harbors and boats. There are many shipwrecks during the winter, as boats get tossed and turned and eventually sink in the fierce, angry waves.

"And then the waves begin to calm, and then the sun comes out from behind the dark clouds and it is springtime again," finished the frog. "Has that satisfied you?"

"Greatly," replied the puddle. "But promise me that you shall return."

"I shall," said the frog, as he began to hop away. "Until next time."

A few days later, the frog returned. He told the puddle of his encounter with a whale when he was a child, and how he had nearly died.

The puddle valued this time listening to the frog immensely, and every time he heard the frog returning, he would rise up with impatience.

This arrangement went on all through the year, even through the winter, when the frog was forced to break a hole in the ice that covered the top of the puddle and speak from the edge instead of splashing around while he talked.

Over time, the frog's visits became less and less frequent, until one evening the puddle asked him if he was alright.

"I am old," said the frog sadly. "I have lived my life. I fear I shall die soon and that this will be our last meeting."

The puddle began to weep, distraught at the fact of losing a great friend, and his source of knowledge of the sea. Suddenly, he had an idea.

"Why, frog, I have the most splendid plan!" said the puddle excitedly. "Is it possible, perhaps, for you to take me in your mouth and bring me down to the sea's edge? I know that your mouth and throat can expand."

The frog, even though he was tired, agreed, and, taking the puddle gently into his mouth, and trying not to swallow, hopped slowly down to the water's edge and dropped the puddle into the sea.

"I am forever grateful," said the puddle. "I shall never forget your kindness to me."

"Goodbye, my friend," said the frog, and hopped quietly away. The puddle never saw him again.

Tumultuous Sea (Acrylic)
Lucy Kershen, 12
Oklahoma

Timepiece

By Daniel Shorten, 11
Ireland

<pre>
                    Timepiece.
          Tick   tock
     Tick   tock
     Back   and   forth
     On   and   on
             On   and   on
                  On and on
</pre>

Every day, same thing, Why?
What folly came over man
to make me? I do not know.
Standing alone now. Quiet.
Telling but not speaking. Why?

Memory Stew

By Lyra Rivera, 11
Illinois

My brain is a stew
When I need something
It is at the bottom
When I don't
It is at the top
Sometimes it is in the middle
Through a struggle
Able to be scooped up

Leaving our Mark (iPhone 6)
Anna Weinberg, 12
Washington, D.C.

Building a Cathedral: An Interview with My Grandfather

Inspired by a conversation with her grandfather, the writer reflects on what makes a meaningful life

By Georgia Marshall, 13
Massachusetts

Almost eight hundred years ago, when stonemasons and architects were building the beautiful cathedrals of Italy, a traveler walked up to a stonemason, the first in a line of three. He asked the man what he was doing, and the stonemason replied dismally that he was cutting stones. Then the traveler walked up to the second stonemason and repeated the same question. The man replied confidently that he was working to become the greatest stonemason of his time. The traveler then turned to the third stonemason and asked what he was doing. The stonemason turned to him and, after a pause, stated that he was a mason, and that he was building a cathedral.

You see, the first stonemason had a mundane relationship with his job. He simply did it to make money. The second stonemason had an ambitious relationship with his job. He wanted to achieve excellence, to be remembered for his work. But it is the third stonemason who represents what is most important. He wanted to make something that would last, that would impact the future and provide a place of peace and refuge for people around the world.

These three perspectives represent three different ways people relate to their work. Some people do a job simply because they have to; others do it because they want to be remembered for it. It is the rare few who do it because it will help and better others in the future. They don't do it for themselves—they do it for the world.

When I first asked my grandfather, Tom Moran, to tell me about his career, he shared this parable. Then he paused for a brief moment to think.

"I had a lot of different jobs," he began. "I started as a social worker. You know, working with people as a counselor, stuff like that. Then the local college asked me to work for one year in the administrative department. After that I just sort of kept working at the college, shifting from job to job. Eventually, I had the role of vice president, then provost."

He explained that he liked to think of his job in three phases, working approximately fifteen years in each. The first phase was in student services and included counseling, student support, and financial aid. The second phase was in academic administration and included things like curriculum development and the running of the college. The third and final phase was teaching. He taught courses in history, English, psychology, and ethics.

"I must've taught at least eighteen different courses and developed, I'd say, twelve of my own," he said. He described his job as "very comprehensive." And he thinks of his work as central to his life rather than as just a career. When considering his relationship with his job, he likes to think that he made an impact on the college, that he improved the educational system and helped make a quality school where young people could discover their place in the world.

As a little kid, I never quite understood what his role within the college was. I always knew that he did something other than teaching. I've come to understand that having gone through so many varying roles within his forty-four years of working at Plattsburgh State University, he shaped the college in many ways.

He created a positive learning environment for so many students, and went on to make the college experience better for everyone with his extensive knowledge and kind demeanor. Over the years he has shown me multiple gifts and tokens of remembrance gifted to him from students and colleagues, each of them coming with some hidden meaning—a story involving a quiet student turned lifelong friend or a wise colleague sharing advice with a younger version of my grandfather.

One of my favorite stories of his time at the college was told to me on a stormy summer night. We were sitting on the couch in his and my grandmother's beautiful Victorian house, which was right across the street from a long line of train tracks—ones with cargo trains that whistle through every morning and evening and that overlook the beautiful, mountainous landscape of Lake Champlain. He looked out of the window at the balmy evening sky, which was starting to rumble with a few thunderclouds.

"This reminds me of when I was in early second or third grade," he said softly. "It was a warm summer afternoon, and our teacher was writing on the chalkboard, when all of a sudden she turned around and peered through the window. She told all of us to drop our pencils and look out the window.

"'What do you see?' she asked. When nobody answered, she told us that a summer storm was coming.

She said to lay our heads on our desks and just listen to the calm, rolling sound of the thunder. She said that 'there is no such thing as beautiful as a thunderstorm on a summer evening or afternoon.'" He repeated the phrase slowly, savoring it.

"I've remembered that phrase ever since that day," he continued. "One day, when I was teaching a college class on a similar summer afternoon, the same thing happened to the sky. Rolling thunder clouds began to slide into the sky, and the sound of thunder rippled through the room.

"'Stop what you're doing, everyone,' I said, walking over to the window. 'Look at the sky. A storm is coming. Everybody lay your heads down on your desks. Listen to the thunder. There is no such thing as beautiful as a thunderstorm on a summer evening or afternoon.'" There was a small pause.

"Wow," I remember saying. "That was beautiful." He nodded in agreement.

"Ever since that day in second or third grade, I've always remembered to stop and listen to the sound of a storm on a summer evening." This made me want to close my eyes and listen to the sound of thunder. And I could imagine a classroom full of students closing their eyes as well, listening to the beautiful sounds.

My grandfather had many influences on his teaching and other work at the college. When asked which one came most prominently to mind, he said that he had so many people in his life, in and out of the college, that had positively influenced him and his knowledge of the world.

"Of course, I could say my parents. My parents were wonderful people who taught me so many things, and if I could have chosen my parents before I was born, I would have chosen them. But I think you mean a deeper connection, someone who I think of as a sort of mentor, who inspires me. And in that sense, the first person that comes to mind is the leader of the college, Dr. Edward Redcay."

He told me that Dr. Redcay, referred to as "Doc" by his friends and colleagues, helped to build the college and transform it into a first-rate educational institution like the ones from which he had received his master's degree and PhD. Dr. Redcay received his bachelor's degree from Dartmouth, his master's degree from Yale, and finally went on to earn his PhD from Columbia University. He worked for a time in Washington, D.C. with Eleanor Roosevelt on school segregation. His research was eventually used by the Supreme Court in their decision to integrate schools.

When he was on his honeymoon, his wife, Lillian, was diagnosed with tuberculosis. They ended up moving up to the Champlain Valley because the mountain air would be good for her lungs. Dr. Redcay began working at SUNY Plattsburgh, the state college in Plattsburgh, New York. He, in the words of my grandfather, "fell in love with working at the college" and was then determined to turn the college into a university at the level of the Ivy League schools from which he had graduated. He shaped the college, turning it into an educational institution most notable for its courses in business administration, nursing, psychology, criminal justice, and more.

"Dr. Redcay stands out to me because he did what I aspired and still aspire to do at the college. He built a strong educational learning system out of a state university and turned into a mentor and great friend to me. After his wife died and he was an old man, we had him over all the time. He came for Christmas, was the subject of a school project for your mom, and even came to do a presentation for your mom's class. He gave everybody cookies with a red K on them. That was his symbol, a red K."

Upon learning about Dr. Edward Redcay, something about the man—perhaps his long list of accomplishments and the impressions he had made on the college, perhaps the sound of his personality or his profound love for Lake Champlain—reminded me of my own grandfather. Like Dr. Redcay, my grandfather is a kind, wise man.

When asked, my grandfather said that, for him, the two most important things in life are to have a meaningful, enjoyable job that combines your passion with your knowledge and to live in a beautiful, inspiring place. In his words, "Part of my sense of the way we create meaning is the way we connect with people, prepare for the future, and appreciate the beauty of life, of the universe. This is what education does. A famous painter, who actually created a lot of paintings set in Lake Champlain, Rockwell Kent, said a phrase that I think directly aligns with my personal values. It goes, 'No task is too small for me. I want to paint the rhythms of eternity.'"

After my grandfather said this, we both paused to think. There is some rhythm to the universe. He and I are drawn to writing and paintings because of how each can capture a moment, a feeling so innocent and beautiful. They can capture the rhythms of eternity.

Perhaps this is what makes me associate Dr. Redcay with my grandfather. They share similar values. They see the world through a similar lens, with an appreciation for education and beauty. They sought to make something that lasts, to leave the college better than they found it. They are both the third stonemason.

When my grandfather graduated with his undergraduate degree, he was merely a dishwasher at the college. But he rose to "build a cathedral." He rose to start a family of caring, intellectual beings. He rose to shape and brighten the minds and souls of so many people, colleagues and students alike. He rose to become a gentle, affectionate man with an appreciation for the "rhythms of eternity." He rose to be my grandfather, more than just my mother's father who happened to have a successful career at the local college, but a mentor. He did, indeed, build his cathedral. And a beautiful one too.

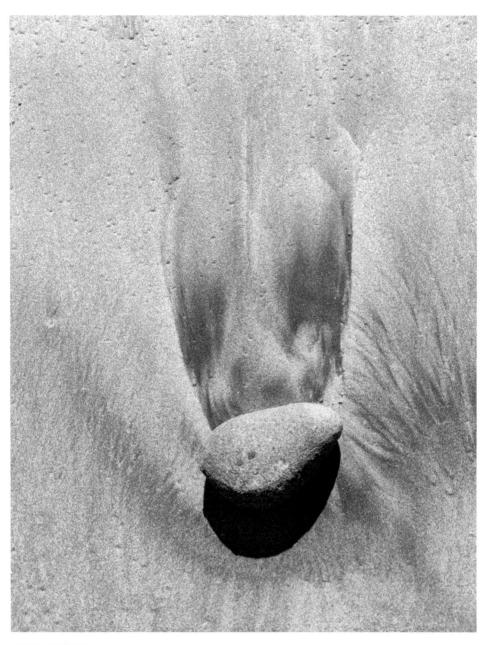

Imprint (OPPO Find X2 Lite)
Savarna Yang, 13
New Zealand

Two Poems

By Elizabeth Merchant, 12
Oregon

Dream

"Let me sleep"
I say
"I'm in the clouds
Today"
"Let me rest"
I state
"I'm in the grass
It's great"
"If I wake
Who knows
When I will see
More snow?"

Abstract

Nothing to do
Just me and you
Everyone is through
Just me and you
Down is light
Day is dark
Night is right
One + one
Is half a ton

Ripples (iPhone 11 Pro)
Sabrina Lu, 13
Virginia

The Little Christmas Tree

A tree, bored with his existence, dreams of another life

By Celia Chen, 10
North Carolina

Once upon a peaceful time, there was a little Christmas tree. He wasn't that much different from the other fir trees on the little mountainside. Day by day he stood there soaking in the golden beams of light cast from the setting sun, soaking up the pure, clean water from the dew-wet soil. *How boring every day is,* thought the little fir tree. *There is nothing to do here but feed myself and feel the earth.*

But one day, the ground shook and pine needles rained down. The sun glinted off the quivering metal blade of an ax. The little tree shook with terror, and as the blade hacked at his trunk, he cried tears of sap. As he was bound in mesh, the ignorant little tree wished to be strung with tinsel and have presents laid at his feet. *How grand I would look, strung with glittering tinsel and having presents laid at my feet like a king; how the other trees would be jealous!*

A family brought him home in a truck, and as he was jerked up and about, he was jolted out of his daydream and went back to being disgruntled. His boughs shook and quaked, raining down needles everywhere. He thought, *How bedraggled I look. How everyone will look down on me. I shall fix myself up once this wretched vehicle stops.* He felt so kingly and royal as he was painstakingly lowered into a pot of water and delighted while these powerful and mighty two-legged people hung elaborate, heavy glimmering orbs. *How the others will look up to me!* he thought.

For many days he sat in a pot of water. Presents were laid at his feet and shiny, glittery tinsel wrapped grandly around his boughs. He felt rather grand, looking down upon these two-legged emperors of the world. Though presently, he felt quite stuffy and dusty; his branches drooped as his essence was slowly leaking out of him. The air had his sweet-smelling soul entwining through it, and his pride gradually diminished. The tree soon wished for rays of sunshine and the moist, dewy soil—to no avail.

Then, one day after Christmas, his wish was granted when he was tossed outside. As he soared through the air, rays of sunshine were thrust upon him every morning, and icy rain and snow plummeted down on him. He cried some more; the foolish tree would always be wishing away at nothing. And so, his last wish was that he could be grand again, and his many babies were rolled by the wandering wind into the forests, to carry out the tale of the little Christmas tree.

On the Other Side of the Wall (iPhone 8)
Tatum Lovely, 12
Pennsylvania

Unconditionally

The narrator finally has enough money to buy the tea set she's coveted—but at what cost?

By Louise Johnson, 11
North Carolina

I should have felt excited, but I didn't.

My mom slid into the driver's seat and started the engine. I didn't look at her. I couldn't. I knew that if I did, all of my bottled-up guilt would come pouring out.

"Y'all excited?" she asked me and my brothers.

"Yeah!" my four-year-old brother, Thor, replied.

"Ma-ma," my youngest brother, Scott, said in broken-up syllables. He was newly one and had just begun to learn how to speak and toddle around.

"Mm-hm," I said. My eyes fell to my lap when she looked at me. I fidgeted in my seat.

"I still can't believe you saved up your money this quickly," she said to me. I couldn't help thinking *I didn't.*

Throughout the car drive, my palms grew sweaty and clammy. I was caught between crying and bursting into nervous giggles. The two-minute drive felt like two hours. I couldn't speak for fear of letting my secret out.

When we arrived at the toy store, Thor was wiggling in his seat and screaming "I'm gonna get the best toy before you!" Scott was completely oblivious to where we were and why we were there. He rocked back and forth in his car seat, sucking his thumb. My mom patiently unbuckled his seatbelt and then moved on to her own.

"I'll wait for you at the checkout counter, okay?" my mom said. "You go get that tea set while I watch Scott."

I nodded, careful to avoid her eyes. I walked into the store, turned the corner, and stopped. I had seen the tea set so many times, but I hadn't had the money for it until now. I walked up to it and double-checked the price tag, even though I had memorized what it said the moment I first saw it. Twenty-one dollars and ninety-nine cents.

Twenty-one dollars and ninety-nine cents I hadn't had until a couple of days ago.

All at once, waves of guilt and remorse crashed inside me, and their blow was harder than anything I had ever felt before. There was nothing I could do to stop it. I remembered how stealing the money felt. I remembered cautiously reaching my hand to the back of the drawer, my fingers clenching around the thin paper. I remembered the guilt

I felt as I counted out ten dollars. I remembered peeking around the corner to make sure the coast was clear. I remembered how the guilt consumed me as I slipped the money into my wallet.

I looked again at the tea set. It was complete with pink-and-white cups, saucers, a teapot, and even a sugar bowl, all in a small wicker basket, perfect for carrying anywhere. How could a six-year-old girl like me not want it? But then again, how could a six-year-old girl like me stand knowing what she had done to get it?

I gritted my teeth and picked the tea set up, excitement, fear, and guilt burning like a raging fire in my stomach. I told myself to put it back, but I couldn't. My greedy, excited body turned toward the cash register, and my stubborn feet started to walk. My guilty hands put it on the checkout counter. Everything was in slow motion as my mother counted out twenty-two dollars and the cashier put them into the cash register.

"Boys, time to go!" my mom called over her shoulder. Everything sped back into regular time. I walked in disbelief back to our car. I had gotten away with it. I had actually done what I had never dreamed of doing. The tea set was mine. The twenty-one dollars and ninety-nine cents had been paid. The funny thing was, I didn't seem to want the tea set anymore. I shook my head. *Don't be silly,* I told myself. *The tea set is yours! You still want it, don't you? Didn't you save all that money for this tea set, and now you don't want it?*

That one question rang in my head. *Didn't I pay all that money? And for what? The tea set was mine. I had paid for it. Hadn't I?*

No. I hadn't. That tea set was not mine, and only I knew it. All the way home, the secret bubbled up inside me, up and up. Every time it bubbled up, it was harder for me to push it back down again.

When we reached home, I picked up the bag the tea set was in. The plastic felt cold and unforgiving against my warm and sweaty palms. I tightened my grip and told my feet to move. My guilt propelled them forward, making me move faster than usual. I needed to get somewhere where I could hide alone, just me and my guilt. I wanted to stuff the tea set under my bed and never see it again. But that would seem suspicious. Usually when we got new toys, we played with them nonstop until bedtime. What would my mom think if she saw me not playing with it? What would she do then? What would I do then?

Once I got inside, I sat down on one of the kitchen stools. The cold metal pressed against my thighs, sending chills through my body. My hands gripped the sides of the stool, and I rocked back and forth. My eyes were glued to the tea set sitting on the island. I pushed down tears and forced myself to keep breathing. I tried my hardest to breathe normally.

My mom walked past me into the office. I peeked around the corner and saw her open a drawer. The same drawer I had "borrowed" ten dollars from a week ago. She pulled out a pack of bills, all ones, together one hundred dollars. Well, one hundred dollars before. Now, ten dollars less. My heart rate quickened. Did she know? If so, how did she know? Had I given anything away?

I pulled myself back around the corner as she started walking back to the kitchen. I could've sworn she could hear my heart thumping in my chest, it was so loud.

She pulled out a stool from under the island and sat down. Without saying a word, she started counting the bills. She counted them multiple times, each time shaking her head as if something was wrong, her brow furrowed. And something was wrong. There were ten less bills than there had been before. I had suddenly gone from having half the money for the tea set to having all the money. I knew what she must have been thinking *How is this possible?* I also knew what I was thinking: *How can she not realize what I've done?*

One tear trickled down my cheek. Once they had started, I couldn't stop them from coming. They ran in streams down my face as I let out sob after sob. My mother looked up from the bills in surprise, and then confusion, and then concern. She walked over to me and put her hand on my back. The warmth of her hand contrasted sharply with the cold, unforgiving shame I was feeling.

"Just take deep breaths," she said in a calm voice.

I inhaled slowly, my breath quivering in the way that it did when I was crying. I repeated this over and over again until my breath had lost some of the quiver and was more steady. I gazed up into my mother's warm blue eyes. Her eyebrows were furrowed in concern, but her voice was steady when she spoke.

"Are you ready to tell me why you were crying?" she asked, and I nodded my head in response.

"I-I-" I stuttered. I burst out into tears again. She continued rubbing my back.

"Just cry it all out," she said. So I did just that.

After crying for a few minutes, I looked my mother in the eye.

"Okay. I-I think I'm ready," I said. She nodded patiently.

"I-I stole your money," I said, bursting out into wrenching sobs all over again. This was it. The moment I had dreaded. The moment where my mother would yell at me, send me to my room, and hate me for the rest of my life. The moment I could never think of again without crying. I couldn't look at my mom. But I had to keep talking.

"I just loved that tea set. I just couldn't wait a whole month to save up enough money for it. And when I found that money in the office drawer, I d-didn't think you would notice if I took only ten dollars. B-but I was wrong," I sobbed. "You did notice, and now you're going to hate me for the r-rest of my whole entire life!" The tears came in streams.

"Louise, you need to calm down," my mom said. I noticed she was still rubbing my back. "I will never hate you. Do you know what unconditional love means?" she asked.

I sniffled. "No," I said, wiping my nose with my sleeve.

My mother looked down at me with a love in her eyes that only a mother could have.

"It means that no matter what you do, no matter what you say, no matter how you feel, I will always love you. Look, it says 'unconditional love' inside my wedding ring. It means that Daddy and I will love each other forever, no matter what. And Daddy and I love you, Thor, and Scott the same way. Unconditionally," she said.

I gazed up into her eyes. "D-does that mean you aren't mad at me?"

"No, I'm not mad at you! In fact, I'm really proud of you," she said.

I looked at her in disbelief. "Really? Why? I did something bad! Why are you proud of me? That doesn't make sense!"

"I'm proud of you because you told me what you did."

My tears stopped.

"It takes a lot of courage to tell somebody what you did. Especially when you love that person a lot, and they love you back. You're scared to lose their love. But Louise," she said, "I will always love you. Always. No matter what. Remember that."

"What are we going to do with the tea set?" I asked.

"Well, it depends. Do you still want it?" she said.

"Yeah, I guess."

"Okay . . . I think I'll keep it in the wrapping paper room until you have enough money to pay back for it. Does that sound good to you?"

"Yes."

I wrapped my arms around her and exhaled shakily.

"Mama?" I asked.

"Uh-huh?" she said.

"I love you."

My mother looked down at me with a love in her eyes that only a mother could have.

"I love you too."

The Smell of Spring

By Kashvi Bhatia,10
New Jersey

As I peered out the window,
the indigo sky,
the snow on the ground
that fell long ago,
surrounded by white,
no hint of sunlight,
I sighed as I looked and climbed into bed,
I woke in the morning, feeling fresh and well fed,
I opened the window,
and to my surprise,
something was different,
I could not tell why.
Taking a sniff of the cold winter air,
I felt a warm little breeze,
full of summer and bees,
fly through my window,
and all through my house,
the smell of spring,
the flowers will sing,
the rain will fall,
the ants will crawl,
the sun will rise,
winter will say goodbye, goodbye,
the birds will fly,
and I rely on spring to come.

Snow Stream (iPhone 8)
Kaeden Kobayashi, 10
California

Snowflakes Are Actually Heavy

Two girls build a snowman

By Abigail Sun, 8
Illinois

One winter day, Emily and Mary went out to play.

Mary said, "We could make a snowman!"

Emily agreed.

Squish splat crunch as they walked through the snow. The spheres were simple.

Emily pointed out, "Are you sure we could carry the head?"

Mary said, "A snowflake is light. We could carry a lot of them."

As they tried to carry it, Mary said angrily, "This is as heavy as a bear! We will never carry it."

But as they kept trying, they finally got it on. They decorated it.

Then the snowman waved at them. They both laughed.

2020's Annoyances (Colored pencil)
Christopher Zhang, 13
Massachusetts

The Deadly Pain

The narrator is subsumed with fear and worry as a mysterious pain fills his stomach

By Misha Joksic, 11
New York

The afternoon sun shined hard on the tall NYC buildings, making them look like gold, as my mom and I walked home. My hand reached out for the door; the peeling black paint fell gently on my fingers as my hand closed around the knob. My mom and I went in and walked the unbearable four-flight walk up to our apartment. My mom took out her keys and wedged them in the lock. It opened. I rushed in, relieved to be free from the sun's heat. My footsteps echoed as I entered my house. My dad was standing near the kitchen counter, busy chopping up some garlic.

My dad wore a dark blue T-shirt with stripes and worn-out jeans. He had a smile on his face, like always, and his stubble was freshly shaved.

"Guess what? My team won three-one in soccer," I rushed to tell my dad. Then I sat down on the brand-new gray couch, took out my iPad, and began to play.

I played for about a half hour until my little sister, Zora, walked through the door wearing a blue dress with butterflies, her wavy dark brown hair falling just beneath her shoulders. She was in preschool and really sweet—

to everyone except me. There was happiness radiating off her every movement. I tried to say hi, but she had already walked away, her hair trailing like a big bar of chocolate.

I got up and got a cup of water, suddenly feeling hot. My head began to hurt and my stomach got little flashes of pain. It felt like the world was spinning and I was in the center of a vortex. The change stunned me.

Why is this happening? What is going on? I thought. Confusion and worry swirled through my head, and though I did not know it at the time, I would feel that way for a long time to come.

The pain in my head and stomach grew, becoming almost unbearable in just a matter of minutes. *It will all be fine. This will be a fine day. I am just tired*, I told myself. But it did not seem likely. Every minute, the pain got worse. It was hard to believe it was a coincidence. I felt like my stomach was about to burst.

I took a deep breath to calm myself down. The aroma from my dad's cooking drifted in the air. The whiff of sizzling bacon spread through the house, making it smell like barbecue.

Not exactly soothing for my rumbling stomach.

I stood up and went to my mom, who was in her room watching a show.

"Can I go lie down?"

"Sure, but are you okay, honey?" my mom asked. Worry spread over her face as fast as a race car.

"I'm fine, Mommy," I managed, though I wasn't sure if this was true.

"Goodnight, love you," she said.

I went to my bed and lay down. My head was hurting and my stomach aching. I slowly fell asleep, hoping that all I needed was rest.

When I woke up, my mom was crouching by my bed, a pained look on her face. My mom was always worried about me and my siblings. Whenever we got even a little bit sick, she agonized, and this was no different.

"Did you sleep well, Mish?" she asked.

"Yep."

"It is dinner soon, honey, so you should go to the kitchen. You don't look that good—your eyes are glassy and you look pale. Are you sure you don't want me to call the doctor and ask for an appointment tomorrow?"

"Yes, Mommy," I said, with a tinge of annoyance in my voice. I stood up and went to the living room. I took a deep breath and sat back down. I was ready to relax, but then I realized I was starving. Now that I was sick, it seemed like I could only see the problems bearing down on me. I looked out the window. A velvety darkness was descending like a blanket over my house.

My dad was still busy cooking. Cooking was, and still is, one of my dad's favorite hobbies, and he loved to do it. He always made these really extravagant meals that took a really long time and that made my mom annoyed because we rarely ate until after our technical bedtime. Once my mom took over cooking, we would eat much earlier, but my dad did not approve of my mom's cooking. "Too greasy," he said.

I started to feel a little better, but the grumbling of my stomach brought me back to my pain.

Why is this happening? I was fine just a few hours ago, I thought in worry.

The pain was changing so suddenly, and I didn't know what to do. I put a blanket over me, even though I wasn't hot.

"Googoogaga!" my one-year-old brother said.

Luka was so cute in his little overalls, his toothless smile revealing some of the mashed peas stuck to his lips.

"Luka!" I said.

I really liked my little brother. The only thing was, he kept on doing what my sister told him to do, and back then Zora did not like me.

I began to feel a bit warmer. I was getting hungry and increasingly impatient waiting for dinner, wondering when the hour would come. But these thoughts didn't distract me for long. Soon the pain made me squirm like a cat chasing yarn. I didn't feel better, and I doubted I ever would.

I sat on the couch for a little while longer until . . .

"Dinner!" my dad shouted in a booming voice, echoing around my house like a megaphone. I stood up and walked to the hexagon-shaped table. My grandpa was an artist, and he had made this table all by himself. The food smelled delicious, and it quenched my hunger just to breathe it in. But I was sick. My head hurt more than ever and my stomach grumbled—but I knew I couldn't eat. We all sat down, the pot of steaming pasta sending its aroma into the air.

"Gonoboolobogoob!" Luka said happily.

I smiled a weak smile at his remark.

"Okay, let's eat!" my dad said loudly.

I hope I can get this down. It was wishful thinking. My hand tightened around the fork as I lifted it into the air and scooped up the pasta and bacon, swirling it around my fork. A burst of flavor exploded in my mouth.

I wonder what movie we will watch tonight. Normally we watch a movie with the whole family, and that night we were going to watch *Fantastic Beasts and Where to Find Them*. We had watched it before, and it was time to watch it again.

"Misha, chew slower!" my dad said, with a tinge of annoyance in his voice.

The food on my plate was delicious, but despite my hunger, I could not eat. The food would not budge. It was like a wall prevented me from swallowing, making me use all my force just to eat a bite. By the end of the meal, I had barely eaten my plate. But somehow, my pain had miraculously seemed to go away. I breathed a sigh of relief and walked to my parents' room (we watched the movie in my parents room sometimes because it was cozier). But as I walked, my pain seemed to resurrect itself. My stomach screamed in pain and my head throbbed.

Why is this happening to me? I knew it was time to tell my parents, but I didn't want them to worry as it was already stressful for them. I took a deep breath and gathered my feelings and strength. I would feel better when I woke up. It will all be fine, I told myself.

I did not know it then, but that would be the mistake that changed the course of that summer, and probably my life. I walked slowly to my parents' room, the darkness casting shadows on the red blanket. The remote for the TV was lying unused, unwanted on the bed. I called everyone for the movie, and footsteps shook the house. Everyone rushed into my parents' room and we started to watch. The movie was very good. Now my pain was subsiding and my eyes were starting to close. I started to drift to sleep.

"Aaaaaah!" I woke up with a start. My pain was worse than ever, my stomach was churning, something was coming up my throat.

"Misha, are you okay?" My parents rushed in. We ran to the bathroom and I started to throw up, pieces of pasta falling into the toilet bowl.

"This is why you chew your food, Misha!" my dad cried in exasperation.

Why is he thinking about me chewing my food and not me throwing up? I thought in pure wonder, and by the look my mom gave my dad, she was thinking the same thing.

My eyes blinked to adjust to the light. I stopped throwing up, but my pain still went on.

"Come on. It will be okay, Misha. Let's go to sleep," my mom said in her soothing voice. So we slowly walked, and though it took a while, my eyes closed, darkness enveloping me once again.

The sunlight wrenched my eyes open as a new day came. After the night I'd had, I was ready for a new start.

"Aaaaaah." I breathed a deep sigh of relief as I stretched my arms.

"Ah!"

Suddenly, a searing pain hit my stomach.

Why is this happening? Again, I wanted to eat but knew I could not. I stood up and the pain hit again, but this time it was a hundred times worse. I fell to the ground, my head throbbing, my stomach feeling as if it were on fire.

"Misha!" my mom yelled.

She came to me and helped me stand up. My dad was there too. My mom put a hand around me as we inched our way to the living room. The pain was unbearable.

"It will be fine, Misha," my dad said in a soothing voice.

"Do you know what happened?" my mom said, her voice trembling with worry.

"No," I replied, my voice quivering.

I inched to the living room as my mom grabbed my hand and opened the door. *We have to go to the doctor,* I thought, and it was clear my mom thought the same thing too. We walked down the stairs in just my pajamas and grabbed the nearest cab we could find. We went straight to the doctor. I didn't know if I was going to survive.

A million thoughts raced through my head, but we didn't talk as we entered the doctor's office. It was a new doctor—my old one has just retired. She didn't recognize me, and in this particular moment, it would have been nice to see a familiar face.

As we entered, I felt the heat leaving my body. I collapsed in the doctor's arms as I crawled onto an examining table. I tried to listen to what she was saying but could barely understand her. My head was throbbing.

"Can you feel this?" the doctor asked as she pressed my stomach. It hurt so much. Flashes of pain came on and off again.

"Yesssssssss," I squealed. The pain made it hard to speak.

"Okay," the doctor said, turning to my mom. "I think he has appendicitis."

"What is that?" I asked.

"There is a pipe in your stomach that doesn't serve much of a function. When it gets infected it can cause severe pain, like what you have now," the doctor explained. The windowless room seemed dark and sinister as what was happening was unfolding in front of me.

"There's only one solution. You will need to have surgery to get it removed, and in order to do that, we need to get you to the hospital now."

I peeled myself off the table, pain searing through my whole body.

What will happen? Will I be fine? Will the surgery be dangerous? Questions whirled through my head and worry clouded my mind. Only danger was apparent now.

"We will take a cab, and get there quickly," my mom said in her calm voice. "No need to worry."

We waited outside the doctor's office. The busy road flashed with cars, not a single cab in sight.

Suddenly my mom caught sight of a yellow car pulling up to the curb with customers getting out.

"Wait for us!" my mom called right as the cab was driving away. We got in and asked to go to NYU Langone Hospital. The driver wore a white T-shirt that said, *A New Day with Surprises.* He had a kind face and trusting eyes. He took off immediately. The big city rushed by in a matter of minutes. But then my stomach seemed to churn and my throat seemed to tense up.

"Mommy, I am going to throw up!"

My mom took a bag from her pocket and I threw up in it just in time.

"I am so sorry," my mom said to the driver.

"It's okay. Let's get him to the ER," the driver said.

We kept on driving as the world spun by. I had no idea where I was or what I was doing there. We finally got out and my mom took out her wallet, pulling out a twenty-dollar bill. She handed it to him and the driver wished me well and drove off, leaving the street empty like a world abandoned. We walked one block to the hospital.

NYU Langone was a big, block-long building with gleaming glass walls reflecting the blue sky and a lobby full of people moving in all directions. I had never been to that hospital before, but my family members would later, and I would go back too, though at the time I didn't know it. We entered, and standing near a white desk made out of marble was a lady with a white doctor's coat and white pants, hair falling just beneath her elbow. She seemed young but had a permanent frown on her face and said in an annoyed voice, "What are you doing here—and please make it quick. I have my lunch break in five minutes."

"We need urgent care for my son. He has . . ."

I blanked out. I couldn't hear her speaking. The world became silent, and my eyes raced around the room. There were big plants that looked like they came from the jungle and a bright green couch which was next to an elevator that led to the rest of the hospital.

"Okay, thank you, thank you," my mom said as the doctor walked off, clearly to her very important lunch break.

"Are you feeling okay, honey?" my mom said, her voice trembling.

"I don't know," I responded.

We rushed up the stairs into a waiting room full of people. We pushed past a chorus of agitated voices. We got through the room and went to a doctor in an old lab coat. She seemed worn out and tired but led us to a hallway with a bed, saying "I'll come back soon." She left us alone again in an unknown place like astronauts on the moon.

I climbed on the bed and my head felt better, but my stomach hurt from every tiny movement. I felt a stabbing pain in my belly.

"It will all be fine, Mishakapishka," my mom said. My face felt like it was on fire as soon as she said it, and not of heat.

Doctors passed by for nearly an hour until finally a group of doctors came and started to look at some papers. One doctor asked me for my name, then went to talk to her colleagues. She had gray hair pulled back in a tight ponytail, and crinkles around her eyes.

What would happen if I needed to get surgery? Worried thoughts swirled around my mind, clouding everything else. I had a fear of surgery, having had an operation when I was just a baby. I could not get another one. No matter what.

"We have evaluated your case and have come to a decision," the doctor said.

I held my breath. Tension filled the room.

"There are two options. You can have surgery to have your appendix removed. Or we can try something new. There is an experimental treatment we are trying, in which we give medicine instead of surgery. It's proving effective in Europe, and we are trying it here. If it's successful, surgical removal of the appendix could be a thing of the past." The doctor left, giving us fifteen minutes to decide my fate.

"What should I do, Mommy?" I asked.

"I don't know, sweetheart. I don't know," my mom replied.

The sun shone hard through the big glass windows, making the floor look like honey as my mom and I contemplated our big decision.

"It's up to you, Mish," my mom said.

I took a deep breath, the sun shining in my eyes, and I spoke . . .

"Okay, if that is your decision," the doctor said. "But there's one more step. If you enter the experiment, you'll be entered into a lottery—half of the participants get surgery (and they act like the control group), and the other half get the medicine. You can participate in the experiment, but I can't guarantee that you won't get operated on."

My heart skipped a beat. I was worried, hopeful, scared, nervous, even a little excited. "If we go ahead with this, the results will come in ten minutes," the doctor finished

Ten minutes later, the doctor reappeared, sharing the good news. "You got it! You're getting the medicine—skipping the surgery!"

I couldn't believe it. Minutes later, the medicine was delivered. Now all I had to do was await my fate and see if the medicine would work. We would know the results in forty-eight hours.

It was late afternoon and my dad came to see how I was doing. I had a room in the pediatric section of the hospital, a small thing with just two beds and a table. Next to my bed was a baby who never stopped crying, and her parents who never stopped arguing.

To pass the time while the medicine set in, I played a game of chess with my dad. I was winning, like always.

"Checkmate!" I said triumphantly

"You won,'" my dad conceded. "I have something for you. It's a Pac-Man game set, to pass the time."

"Thank you, thank you, thank you!" I squealed.

My dad's birthday was coming up, and I couldn't believe he was the one giving me a present. For a long time, I was happy and excited—everything was working out.

I got onto the bed just as dinner came in. It was bland rice with chicken and milk. I ate it without tasting anything. My pain was lowering, but not by much. I could walk a little, not a lot, but at least I was improving.

By the time I finished eating, it was night, and with a groan and a lot of pain I tried to close my eyes. I lay my head on the pillow and allowed my dad's voice to fill my head. It was nice to have my dad here, sleeping in the room with me, helping me have a peaceful recovery. At last, I fell asleep.

When I woke up, the pain had subsided. "Mommy is going to come today to be with you," my dad said. I nodded because it was what I wanted. I was going to make him a birthday card, so he couldn't be there. When my mom arrived, I swallowed the remaining pain that was circulating through my body and started writing a birthday card. It was full of love and drawings and warm wishes for him to have the best birthday ever.

After I made the card, my mom took me to a game room. It was amazing. There was a Nintendo Wii, where you could play games. There were tons of kids, and we all could play together. I played a racing game (I lost). A clown visited. It was so fun I forgot how much pain I'd had and how much stress I felt.

But as I played games with other kids, I also saw something else. The room was filled with kids who didn't have hair, who had wires attached to their heads. Kids who were in wheelchairs. And kids who were really skinny and didn't look strong. That's when it hit me: while I would be leaving this hospital, many of these kids wouldn't be so lucky. They would spend days, weeks, maybe even years dealing with pain like the pain I had felt, and with the worry. For them, this wouldn't be over in a matter of hours.

In the end, the medicine did its job. I got better. I got to go home. But many of the other kids I saw did not, kids who had illnesses that medicine couldn't heal. It was then that I realized a simple truth: that every now and then, everyone has a responsibility to help.

We live in a world that is not perfect, where you can get sick without realizing it, for no fault of your own. And when you're not well, you need the care of people who love you, and even strangers who can make you feel better. We owe it to each other to help one another, when we are feeling healthy and when we are sick. We are in this work together, and if we help one another, nothing is going to get in our way— not even appendicitis.

Two Poems

By Shivanshi Dutt, 12
New Jersey

Armor

Acting silly, having fun,
  Being someone I'm truly not.

The sun is saying goodbye,
  The sky is putting on a show—
Daffodil yellow, sky blue,
  And pink the shade of flamingo feathers.

I exit the house,
  My shield slowly melting away,
My permanent smile turning into a straight line,
  My benevolent demeanor changing.

Away from people,
  I put down my armor.
Becoming someone
  People never see.

Are We Doing Enough?

Beautiful maple trees.
Little flowers brush against my knees.
The sun is shining bright as an LED light,
And fluffy clouds are in sight.

My raven-black hair billows in the wind,
The strands of hair tickling my chin.

As I stand there, I notice the rough trees
And shiny green leaves.

But I also spot
Big aluminum cans
And plastic bags.

As I stand motionless,
I wonder,
Are we doing enough to show the Earth our love?

Head in the Clouds (Ink)
Emily Yu, 14
Hong Kong

The Magic Desk

An ode to a desk

By Noah Xia, 9
New Jersey

It's heavy, old, and has scribbles all over its body. But it is mine, and I love it.

My desk has been with me for at least three years. It used to be my dad's, but then my parents gave it to me. When I got my desk, it was pretty clean, but it didn't stay that way. It has paint smudges on top and underneath. My little brother even drew on it. But the important part was the creative adventures I had with it.

Unlike humans, my desk won't get mad if I don't do something correctly or if I mess it up (but my mom and dad might). It will keep silent so I can move on. Once I even tried to draw a mini mural of a mermaid and narwhal on it, but it's not there anymore. I remember that around the color pencil case on my desk, there was a rectangular-ish outline of paint. When my dad saw it, he washed away the smudges on the desk. I was very sad when he did. If you look at the bottom of my desk, you will see lots of marks because I used to wipe the things on my hands (like dirty paint) under the table.

But setting the messes aside, it has changed a lot. There used to be folders, but now there is a mess box my dad gave me for my stuff. There used to be a corkboard hanging next to my desk, now there isn't.

Yet some things haven't changed so much. For example, my pencil cases haven't really moved. They have, of course, been stored into boxes, but the boxes got plopped right back onto my desk.

My desk itself has moved, though, from the living room to the moving truck to one of the smaller rooms in the new house, and finally to its resting place in my room.

Although my desk appears to be a mess, what's more important are the things I do there. Sometimes my desk is my art studio, with my paintbrushes and paints and papers. In fact, I did most of my paintings on my desk. Other times, I make jewelry on my desk. I make the necklaces and bracelets my friends and I wear now. Or, my desk is a crafting table, with my journals and notebooks and all the materials I make things with.

As you see, my desk has been my companion for a while. Though in the beginning, I wanted to keep the mess as I was too lazy to clean it up, now I am the one to clean it up.

I've realized that even if I do clean things sometimes now that I'm older and getting more like my dad, my creativity will never be washed away. Not by water, not by rain, not by coffee. Messes are my way to express myself. Besides, even if I do clean it, a few days later it'll be messy again!

Countryside (Watercolor)
Crystal Fu, 11
New York

A Quiet Neighborhood

By Kimberly Hu, 9
Oregon

A quiet neighborhood seemed empty,

yet it was the fullest it could be.

Even if ones weren't out,

they were enjoying peace and love

with their friends and family.

Even if the outside seemed empty

it was very full.

Animals like birds and squirrels

skittered and flew

with a cool breeze that surrounded,

thriving in a promising

nature-full environment.

Peace fluttered place to place,

filling everywhere with itself.

Even if it was so full,

so full,

never yet to be completely full.

A quiet neighborhood would

always welcome

more to be

in such a wonderful place,

such a wonderful place.

Such a wonderful place

ain't need anything

but wonderful creatures.

Nothing ain't not wonderful

if it just cherishes life.

Such a wonderful place needn't be a quiet neighborhood.

Such wonderful creatures needn't be people and birds and squirrels.

A loud neighborhood, maybe,

but maybe

a forest,

a meadow,

a city without harm.

a desert, even,

a humble rural,

any place could fit

the wonderful atmosphere

of beautiful nature.

A gorilla, haha,

a dog,

a cat,

a horse,

or maybe even

a snake—

everything

is beautiful

in any possible way.

Sometimes

people just misread

the eyes of

some creature,

but all

are equal

in a beautiful world,

and

some places,

like a quiet neighborhood,

some creatures,

like a seemingly scary spider,

can have just as much

peace

and love

without fear

and with courage,

without needing

to shrink back into the shadows,

but with

strength,

kindness,

bravery,

darkness to light

and a heart

to a small world like so,

in just a humble place,

in just a wonderful place,

with just wonderful creatures

and everything that life could give

which could be found

in such an ordinary,

fanciless place—but with peace

and love.

A Moment of Peacefulness (Colored pencil, pigment liner)
Tutu Lin, 13
Texas

Highlight from Stonesoup.com

from the Stone Soup Blog

from "Flamethrower"

By Jacob Chan, 11
New York

I was almost eleven in the warm, windy fall of the year 2019 when my baseball team, the Bulldogs, was playing in the little league semifinals. But still, I couldn't help but want to crawl under my bed where I would be safe. I couldn't even bear to glance at the opposing pitcher's deep blue eyes. His fastball was so fast that if you rode on it around a highway, you would get fined for speeding.

My team crammed in the dugout before the game started, each of us getting to know one another way more than we wanted to. I swear I smelled vomit on the jersey of one of my teammates.

"Listen up, Bulldogs!" my coach, Adam, began to yell. "It's the semifinals—if we don't win this, each of you owes me five laps around the field!"

Everyone groaned. Everyone, with the exception of me and a few other boys. Not that we wanted to run laps, mind you, but because we were staring at the five-foot-seven kid on top of the mound warming up. He was literally throwing fireballs into the catcher's rusty old well-padded brown mitt, with the glove strings tightly knotted. For a second, I didn't care about the ten-pound gold trophy sitting on the table behind the dugout that would be handed out to the winner. I just cared about not getting plunked in the face by a seventy-mile-per-hour fastball thrown by the eleven-year-old Godzilla. Alright, alright, call me a scaredy cat, but let's face it—you would be freaking out too.

The tap of Bowen Orberlie, one of my teammates, brought me back to reality.

"Earth to Jacob!" he said into my ear. I shook, and glanced up at my coach, who was throwing darts out of his eyes to every single one of my teammates. Glancing down at a torn-up sheet of paper, he began to scream the starting lineup aloud, with little tiny molecules of spit coming out of his wide-open mouth as he spoke.

"Chan, leading off!" he yelled at the top of his lungs, so loud you would have thought he was my cousin after watching the New York Mets lose. I froze. To be honest, I should have been proud of my nearly .370 on-base percentage that had gotten me the role of batting leadoff in the semifinals, but—I. Did. Not. Want. To. Face. This. Pitcher.

The rest of the lineup was a blur. I couldn't think straight. Trembling, I grabbed my Rawlings blue-and-silver bat and stepped outside the dugout. I began to take some dry swings—you know, the swings that coaches and parents always say will "help you get better."

You can read the rest of Jacob's piece at https://stonesoup.com/young-bloggers/.

About the Stone Soup Blog

We publish original work—writing, art, book reviews, multimedia projects, and more—by young people on the Stone Soup Blog. You can read more posts by young bloggers, and find out more about submitting a blog post, here: https://stonesoup.com/stone-soup-blog/.

Honor Roll

Welcome to the Stone Soup Honor Roll. Every month, we receive submissions from hundreds of kids from around the world. Unfortunately, we don't have space to publish all the great work we receive. We want to commend some of these talented writers and artists and encourage them to keep creating.

Visit the Stone Soup Store at Stonesoupstore.com

At our store, you will find . . .

- Current and back issues of *Stone Soup*
- Our growing collection of books by young authors, as well as themed anthologies and the *Stone Soup Annual*
- High-quality prints from our collection of children's art
- Journals and sketchbooks

. . . and more!

Finally, don't forget to visit Stonesoup.com to browse our bonus materials. There you will find:

- More information about our writing workshops and book club
- Monthly flash contests and weekly creativity prompts
- Blog posts from our young bloggers on everything from sports to sewing
- Video interviews with *Stone Soup* authors

. . . and more content by young creators!

CPSIA information can be obtained
at www.ICGtesting.com
Printed in the USA
JSHW080350051122
32626JS00001B/3